Growler
the Wolf Pup

by Jenni Bidner

Glad to meet you!

I am Growler.

This is
Howler.

Now meet
Prowler.

They're my sister
and my brother,

And we look
like one another.

Wolves have families
just like you —

Moms and dads,
aunts and uncles too!

We live in a cave called a den.
It's one room that fits about ten.

At three weeks old, we learn to walk.
A grunt or growl is how we talk.

Mom has no arms to hold a pup.
So this is how she picks me up!

When days are hot
we dig a hole.

It's a cool place
for us to roll.

Naughty Prowler
wakes up our dad.

He shows his teeth
to say he's mad!

At five weeks old,
I'm growing strong.

And now my legs
are getting long!

Pups like to wrestle
in the dirt.

It's great fun
and we don't get hurt!

When little Howler starts a song,
Brothers and sisters sing along.

Soon the whole family joins the fun.
Our howl is sung by everyone!

We do not like
to share our meat.
We growl and snarl
when we eat.

We both want
this piece for dinner–
The strongest pup
is the winner.

When we finish our dinner meat,
A crunchy bone is a yummy treat.

We do not mind the rain and mud.
Don't you want a wet wolfie hug?

I play with Howler on some trees,

While Prowler chases bumble bees.

We love to play
tug-of-war...

Then we wrestle ...
and run some more!

This playing makes us want to sleep,

We snuggle up in one big heap.

Good-night my friends,
it's time for bed.

The pages here
have all been read.

Thanks for sharing
my Growler book.

Come back soon
for another look!

More About Wolves

BABY WOLVES: Wolves are born in litters, usually with 3 to 6 puppies. They are born with their eyes closed. At about three-weeks old, when they can see and walk, they come out of their den. When the puppies wander too far away from the den, mother wolves sometimes gently carry the babies back in their mouths.

WOLF LANGUAGE: Wolves communicate in a similar way to dogs. They make all sorts of sounds from grunts and growls, to barks and howls. They also communicate through body language. Things like tail position, eye contact and raised hairs along the shoulder and spine (hackling) can send a very clear message to other wolves. Author Jenni Bidner's Bergh Award winning book, "*Is My Dog a Wolf?*" compares dogs to wolves, showing how they are similar in some ways and very different in others.

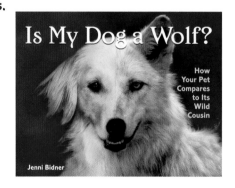

Is My Dog a Wolf?
How Your Pet Compares to Its Wild Cousin
Jenni Bidner

WOLF FOOD: A wolf's primary food is meat, such as deer, or smaller animals like rabbits. If meat is scarce, they will occasionally eat berries and other fruits. Some people are surprised to learn that wolves do not eat breakfast, lunch and dinner. Sometimes they do not eat for days. But when they are lucky enough to find or catch a big meal, an adult wolf can eat more than 20 pounds of food— that is the same amount as eating about 80 hamburgers in one meal!

WOLF PLAY: Wolf puppies like to play. They run and chase each other, and do a lot of pretend fighting. This teaches them important wolf social skills, and helps them grow strong. They also practice pouncing on sticks and leaves as a way to learn to hunt.

DOGHEROES
Saving Lives and Protecting America
Jen Bidner

HUNTING: Wolves have an incredibly good sense of smell. Their ability to smell is much, much better than people's, and even better than dogs, Wolves use their sense of smell to hunt. They can sniff the ground to figure out if a deer has recently passed through the area, and then can follow the path it took just by smell! They can also raise their nose in the air and smell a deer's scent on the wind.

Dogs can also use their noses to follow scent. Author Jenni Bidner uses her two dogs Quinto and Liebchen ("Little-One") to find lost or missing people. Just like a wolf smelling where a deer has traveled, these dogs have been trained to smell where a person has walked. You can learn more about Search & Rescue dogs in her book "Dog Heroes: Saving Lives & Protecting America," or visit the website of her search unit, ILL-WIS Search Dogs at www.sardog.com.

GROWLER'S HOME: Growler and his pack live at the Wildlife Science Center (WSC) in Minnesota. The WSC is a non-profit research and educational facility that has become a safe haven for wolves like Growler. To learn more about visiting the WSC or supporting their work with wolves, visit their website at www.wildlifesciencecenter.org.

At the Wildlife Science Center, visitors can learn about wolves and other wild animals. The WSC is open for tours. They also offer other wonderful wolf adventures for children including Wolf Howl Bonfires, overnight camping experiences, Scout badge programs, and summertime day and overnight camps. The WSC also helps scientists do research projects that will help wild wolves in the future.

Glossary

DEN: A den is a wolf home, often made by digging a cave into the ground or the side of a hill.

GROWL: A growl is a low rumbling sound that sounds like "grrrrrh". Wolves (and dogs) use growls to warn others that they are protective of something or someone. For example, one wolf may growl at the rest of the pack to keep them from taking away his food.

HOWL: A howl is a wolf's "song". It sounds different than a bark. It is a long call that sounds like "ah-woo-woo-woooo." It is used to call to each other over distances. Wolves also seem to enjoy howling together as a bonding experience for the entire pack. Can you howl like a wolf? Give it a try!

PACK: A pack is a group of wolves that lives together like a family and help each other survive. It can include the parents, puppies, older sisters and brothers, aunts and uncles, and also unrelated wolves.

Index

10 9 8 7 6 5 4 3 2 1
Printed in the USA
© 2013 Ajax Acres
For more information visit our website at www.AjaxAcres.com and
www.JenniBidner.com

First Edition
Published by Ajax Acres, 3104 Walkup Road, Crystal Lake IL 60012
Text and photography (c) 2013 Jenni Bidner

Manufactured in the United States.

All rights reserved.

ISBN: 978-0-9892981-0-0

Library of Congress Control Number: 2013907269

If you have questions or comments about this book, please contact info@ajaxacres.com. For information about custom editions, special sales, premium and corporate purchases, please contact our Special Sales department at info@ajaxacres.com.